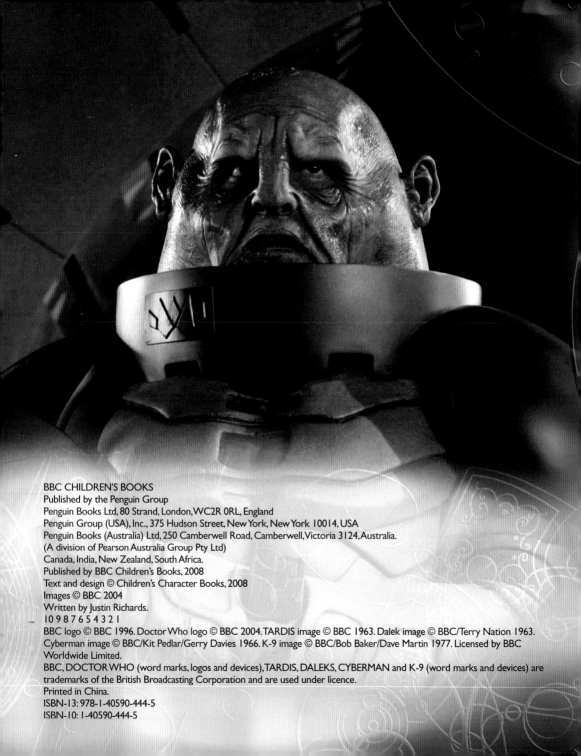

BBC CHILDREN'S BOOKS
Published by the Penguin Group
Penguin Books Ltd, 80 Strand, London, WC2R 0RL, England
Penguin Group (USA), Inc., 375 Hudson Street, New York, New York 10014, USA
Penguin Books (Australia) Ltd, 250 Camberwell Road, Camberwell, Victoria 3124, Australia.
(A division of Pearson Australia Group Pty Ltd)
Canada, India, New Zealand, South Africa.
Published by BBC Children's Books, 2008
Text and design © Children's Character Books, 2008
Images © BBC 2004
Written by Justin Richards.
10 9 8 7 6 5 4 3 2 1

Printed in China.
ISBN-13: 978-1-40590-444-5
ISBN-10: 1-40590-444-5

CONTENTS

They might look like dumpy potato-heads, but the Sontarans are a brutal race of warriors dedicated to warfare. They have been at war with the Rutans for thousands of years, neither side gaining a lasting advantage in the struggle. But the Sontarans will attack anyone if they think they can gain an advantage in the Sontaran-Rutan war.

The Sontarans come from the high-gravity planet, Sontar. They reproduce by cloning - at a rate of a million every four minutes in great muster parades. They are all identical in appearance.

Despite their ruthlessness and brutality, the Sontarans have a keen sense of honour. Nothing makes a Sontaran more angry than to suggest he is without honour, or that he has failed in his mission.

They even see their greatest weakness as a strength because a Sontaran can only be stunned by a blow to the probic vent. Since the probic vent is a small hole at the back of the neck, the Sontarans believe this means they must always face their enemies.

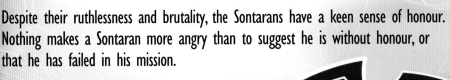

They might not have defeated the Rutans yet, but the Sontarans are formidable adversaries and amongst the most feared warrior races of the Universe.

Name:	Sontaran
Species:	Cloned warrior
Height:	1.6m (5'6")
Home Planet:	Sontar
Weaponry:	A choice of deadly guns and artillery
Protection:	Battle armour
Communication:	Universal translation device
Weakness:	Probic vent (at the back of the neck) is very sensitive
Greatest Enemies:	The Rutan Host and the Doctor
Battle Cry:	Sontar-ha! Sontar-ha! Sontar-ha!

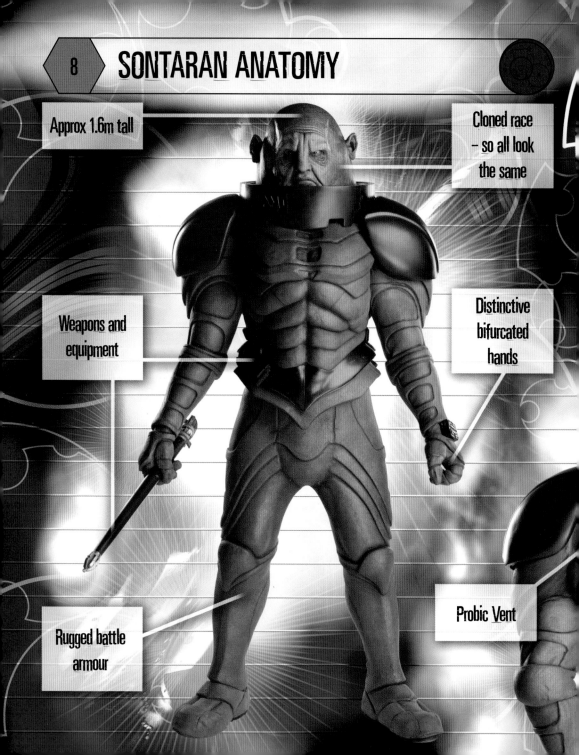

Approx 1.6m tall

Cloned race – so all look the same

Weapons and equipment

Distinctive bifurcated hands

Rugged battle armour

Probic Vent

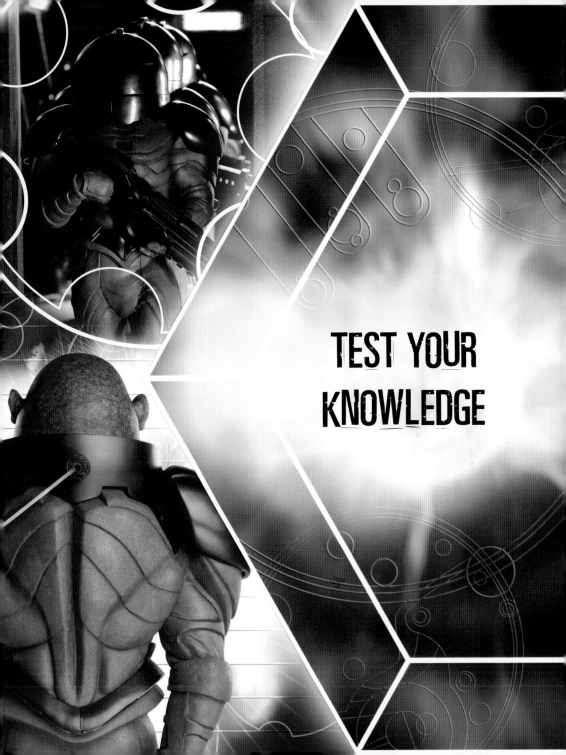

TEST YOUR KNOWLEDGE

GENERAL STAAL

Like all Sontarans, General Staal of the Tenth Sontaran Battle Fleet was a dedicated soldier. Bred to be a Sontaran commander, he had highly-developed strategic skills, a keen sense of honour and a lust for glory. General Staal was put in charge of the Sontaran attempt to turn Earth into a Clone World in the early 21st century by Sontaran High Command.

Victorious in all his previous campaigns and battles, the General was known as Staal the Undefeated. But he was killed when the attempt to take over Earth failed and his warship was blown up.

COMMANDER SKORR

Commander Skorr reported directly to General Staal and was second in command of the Tenth Sontaran Battle fleet. Known as Skorr the Bloodbringer, he was every bit as ruthless and determined as his commanding officer.

General Staal entrusted the vital raid on the ATMOS Factory to Commander Skorr. But Skorr was ultimately defeated and shot down by Colonel Mace of UNIT.

LIEUTENANT SKREE

In command of the day-to-day running of General Staal's flagship, Lieutenant Skree remained loyal to his general - and to the Sontaran code of war — right to his death when the flagship was destroyed.

As well as coordinating the attack on the ATMOS Factory, he was responsible for planning the weapons strike that would destroy all life on Earth.

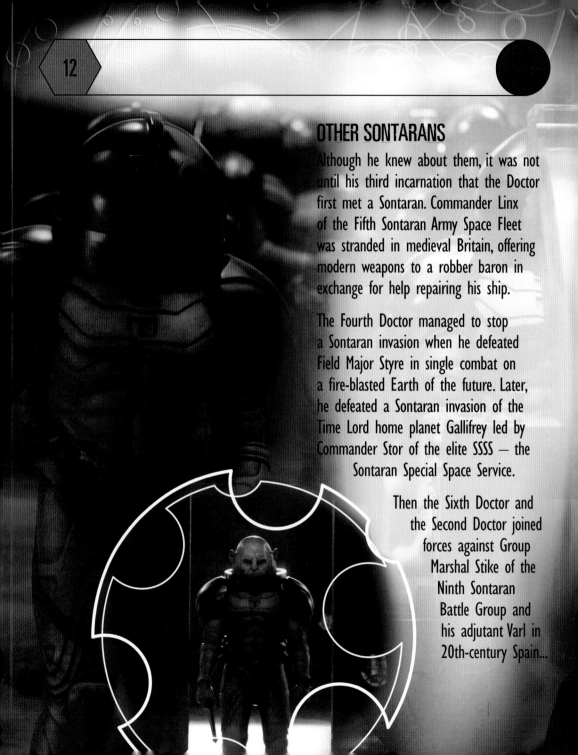

OTHER SONTARANS

Although he knew about them, it was not until his third incarnation that the Doctor first met a Sontaran. Commander Linx of the Fifth Sontaran Army Space Fleet was stranded in medieval Britain, offering modern weapons to a robber baron in exchange for help repairing his ship.

The Fourth Doctor managed to stop a Sontaran invasion when he defeated Field Major Styre in single combat on a fire-blasted Earth of the future. Later, he defeated a Sontaran invasion of the Time Lord home planet Gallifrey led by Commander Stor of the elite SSSS — the Sontaran Special Space Service.

Then the Sixth Doctor and the Second Doctor joined forces against Group Marshal Stike of the Ninth Sontaran Battle Group and his adjutant Varl in 20th-century Spain...

LUKE RATTIGAN

Teenage technology genius Luke Rattigan invented the Fountain Six Search Engine when he was just 12 years old. He became a millionaire almost overnight as a result, and later opened the Rattigan Academy — a private school educating hand-picked students from all over the world.

But Rattigan was in league with the Sontarans. In return for his help producing and distributing the ATMOS system, he thought the Sontarans would take him and his gifted students to a new planet to start a new Earth...

But the Sontarans just used Rattigan, with no intention of helping him. Betrayed and disillusioned, Rattigan destroyed the Sontaran warship, killing General Staal and ending the Sontaran threat to Earth.

TEST YOUR KNOWLEDGE

THE RUTANS

THE WAR

From the cold, icy planet of Ruta 3, the Rutans evolved in the sea before adapting to land. They look like large, glowing green jellyfish with tentacles that can give a massive electric shock — enough to kill. The Rutans are the sworn enemies of the Sontarans, and the Rutan Empire has been at war with the Sontarans for thousands of years.

The Rutans developed a metamorphosis technique that allowed them to take on the appearance of other creatures with which they had come into contact.

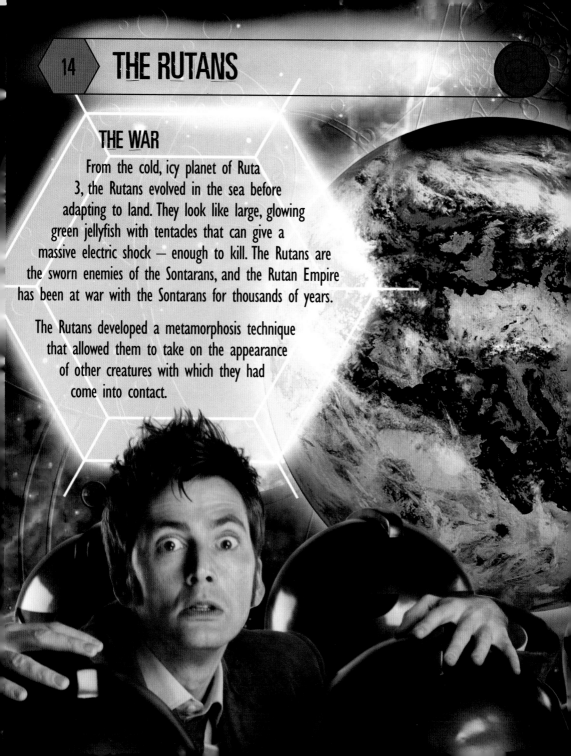

EARTH

Although Commander Linx was ambushed by a squadron of Rutan fighters close to Earth in medieval times, it wasn't until centuries later that the planet's strategic position became important.

A Rutan expedition to Earth in the early 20th century concluded the planet was too dangerous to attack, after the Doctor destroyed the Rutans that attacked the Fang Rock lighthouse.

Despite a brief mission to 20th century Earth by Group Marshal Stike and his adjutant Varl, it was in the far future that the Sontarans assessed Earth as a military target. They also experimented on humans to see if they were fit for war. They concluded that it was not in their interests to attack — again, after the Doctor intervened.

With the help of UNIT and his friends Donna and Martha, the Doctor defeated a Sontaran attempt to turn Earth into a clone world...

OTHER SONTARAN ENEMIES

THE DOCTOR

The Doctor is the last of the Time Lords, a traveller in time and space. He can change his appearance — when his body is worn out or damaged he can change into a new one. Travelling through space and time in his TARDIS, and with the help of various companions, the Doctor fights against evil and injustice.

The Sontarans have found their plans thwarted by the Doctor on several occasions — on one occasion they even dared to invade Gallifrey, the planet of the Time Lords.

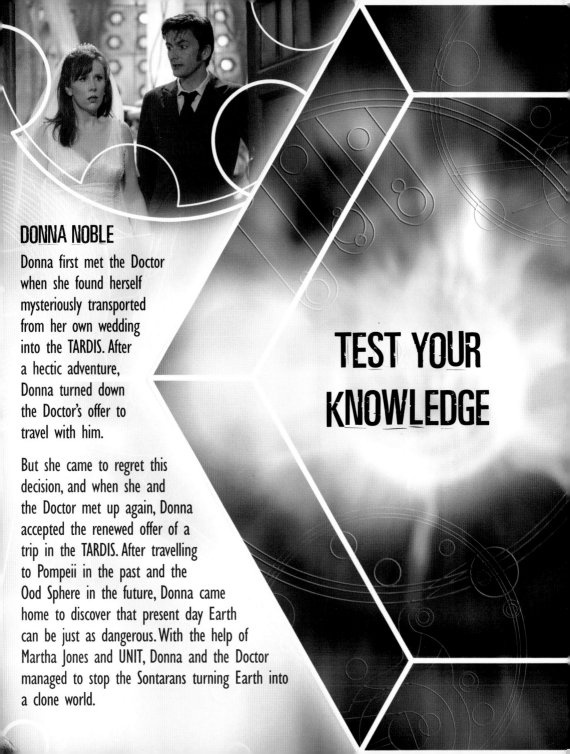

DONNA NOBLE

Donna first met the Doctor when she found herself mysteriously transported from her own wedding into the TARDIS. After a hectic adventure, Donna turned down the Doctor's offer to travel with him.

But she came to regret this decision, and when she and the Doctor met up again, Donna accepted the renewed offer of a trip in the TARDIS. After travelling to Pompeii in the past and the Ood Sphere in the future, Donna came home to discover that present day Earth can be just as dangerous. With the help of Martha Jones and UNIT, Donna and the Doctor managed to stop the Sontarans turning Earth into a clone world.

TEST YOUR KNOWLEDGE

MARTHA JONES

Martha Jones used to travel with the Doctor. She left him to stay with her family after she helped the Doctor and Captain Jack Harkness defeat the Master. When the Doctor and Donna meet her again, Martha is working with UNIT to investigate the ATMOS system.

Although she saw incredible things and faced many dangers when she was with the Doctor, nothing quite prepares Martha for meeting herself. The Sontarans create a clone copy of Martha who infiltrates UNIT and betrays them. The real Martha remains in a coma while the clone is at large. But the clone dies when the Doctor revives the real Martha.

UNIT

The Doctor has worked with UNIT — which stands for UNified Intelligence Taskforce — many times over many years. UNIT is a worldwide force that deals with alien incursions and other extraordinary threats to Earth.

UNIT's Operation Blue Sky is a raid on the ATMOS Factory, led by Colonel Mace. But they are almost too late to stop the Sontaran stratagem. The UNIT force manages to avoid the worst effects of the ATMOS gas by blowing it away using the massive engines of its flying aircraft carrier Valiant. Colonel Mace and his troops then fight off the Sontaran invaders, giving the Doctor time to defeat the Sontarans.

ATMOS

The ATMospheric Omission System developed by Luke Rattigan uses an ionising nano-membrane carbon dioxide converter to reduce CO_2 emissions to zero. It also provides satellite navigation and other on-board motoring systems. With Rattigan's help, the Sontarans have made sure the system is fitted to 800 million cars across the whole world.

UNIT becomes suspicious when over fifty people die at the exact same time under the same circumstances all across the world. The Doctor realises that ATMOS uses advanced alien technology.

In fact, ATMOS is a Sontaran weapon. When activated, it emits a gas called Caesofine Concentrate from the cars' exhausts. One part Probic 5 to two parts Bosteen, the gas is a clonefeed. It will change the Earth's atmosphere so it is suitable for the Sontarans to clone billions of troops. But the gas is poisonous and will also make it uninhabitable for humans.

Luckily, the gas is volatile and the Doctor is able to burn it off, thwarting the Sontarans' plans.

TEST YOUR KNOWLEDGE

CLONES

The Sontarans are a race of clones. They can create a million more Sontarans every four minutes in huge Muster Parades on dedicated clone worlds. With such vast numbers of troops available so quickly, they can sustain huge losses in battle against their sworn enemies – the Rutans.

As well as cloning themselves, the Sontarans can also create clones of other species. To create a clone of an individual human, they need access to the original person. They clone several UNIT soldiers to defend vital areas of the ATMOS Factory and spy on UNIT. They also clone Martha Jones.

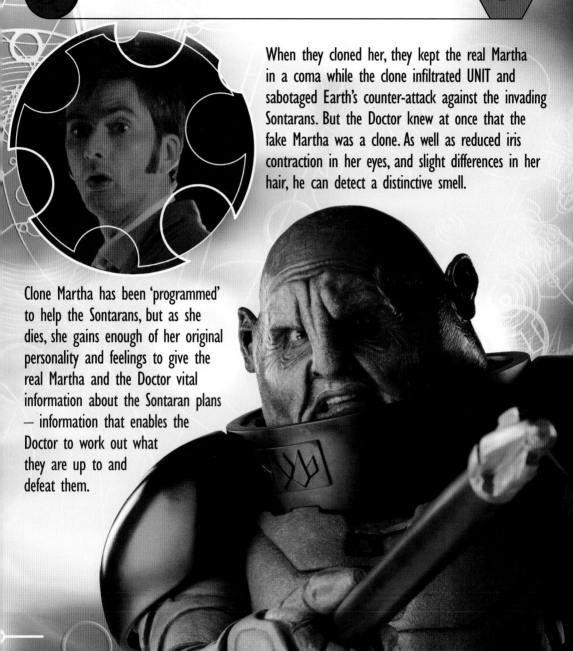

When they cloned her, they kept the real Martha in a coma while the clone infiltrated UNIT and sabotaged Earth's counter-attack against the invading Sontarans. But the Doctor knew at once that the fake Martha was a clone. As well as reduced iris contraction in her eyes, and slight differences in her hair, he can detect a distinctive smell.

Clone Martha has been 'programmed' to help the Sontarans, but as she dies, she gains enough of her original personality and feelings to give the real Martha and the Doctor vital information about the Sontaran plans — information that enables the Doctor to work out what they are up to and defeat them.

SONTARAN WARSHIPS

A race that lives for war has many terrible weapons at its disposal. None of these have more firepower than the fearsome Sontaran warships. Huge, majestic, and lethal, Sontaran warships are armed with a variety of weapons, including enough missiles to destroy entire planets. They go into battle in a distinctive arrow-shaped formation.

General Staal's flagship has teleport ability — a direct link to locations like the Rattigan Academy as well as remote systems that Staal uses to bring the TARDIS on-board.

The ship is destroyed when Luke Rattigan operates the Doctor's atmospheric converter, recalibrated so it will ignite the air in the Sontaran ship. As the ship burns, its missiles explode and the Sontaran invasion force is completely destroyed.

SONTARAN SCOUTSHIPS

A Sontaran warship is equipped with scoutships that can detach from the main craft for short range expeditions. The Sontaran scoutship is spherical, spinning its way through space.

The Sontarans also use scoutships for clandestine operations as they are small enough to avoid Rutan — and other — detection systems. Incredibly powerful for their size, they can also be used to spearhead attacks on stationary targets like spacestations. Some more advanced scoutships can be placed in 'clear' when they have landed — making them invisible.

TEST YOUR KNOWLEDGE

SONTARAN STRATEGIES

PREVIOUS STRATEGIES

The Doctor encountered the Sontarans several times before he foiled their attempt to turn the Earth into a Sontaran Clone World.

The Second Doctor had to be rescued by his own Sixth incarnation when he was kidnapped by the Sontaran Group Marshal Stike and held prisoner in Spain. Stike hoped to learn the secret of time travel from the Doctor.

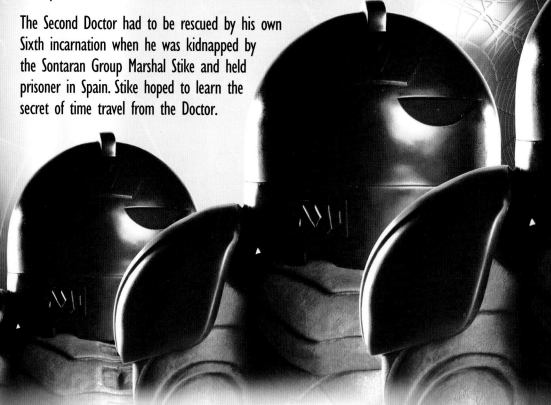

In fact the Sontarans soon obtained limited time travel ability. The Third Doctor was called in by UNIT to investigate when key scientists went missing. Helped — for the first time — by journalist Sarah Jane Smith, he discovered the scientists were in Medieval England. Sontaran Commander Linx was using an Osmic Projector to kidnap scientists from the future to help repair his damaged ship.

In his fourth incarnation, the Doctor next met the Sontarans in the far future, when Field Major Styre was assessing how well humans might deal with a Sontaran attack. The Doctor defeated Styre in single combat and the attack was called off.

The Fourth Doctor encountered the Sontarans again — when they invaded the Time Lords' home planet of Gallifrey! Having been accidentally elected President, it was up to the Doctor — helped by his friend Leela and robot dog K-9 — to organise resistance to the invasion. He dematerialised the Sontaran Commander Stor with a deadly Demat Gun, and the Sontaran invasion was defeated.

THE ATMOS STRATEGY

Again, UNIT was involved from the outset in foiling the Sontaran ATMOS Strategem. Suspicious of a series of identical deaths caused by the ATMOS system installed in cars across the world, UNIT raided the Atmos factory.

The Doctor and Donna teamed up with UNIT and the Doctor's friend Martha Jones to discover the involvement of the Sontarans, led by General Staal. Despite UNIT soldiers being hypnotised and Martha Jones being replaced by a Sontaran clone, the Doctor and Donna were able to discover the truth of the Sontaran plan.

The Sontarans were going to use the ATMOS system installed in millions of cars to emit a gas that would suffocate all humans. But the gas would create the ideal conditions for Earth to become a Clone World — where the Sontarans could create millions of cloned troops to battle their ancient enemy, the Rutans.

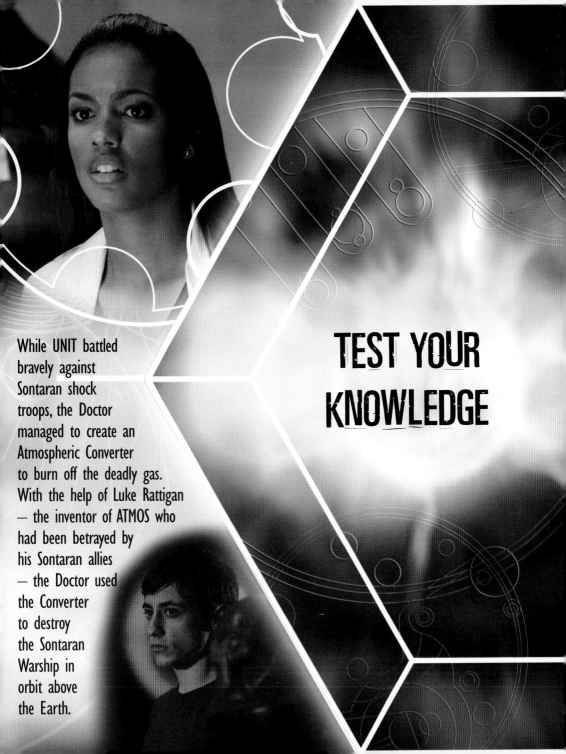

While UNIT battled bravely against Sontaran shock troops, the Doctor managed to create an Atmospheric Converter to burn off the deadly gas. With the help of Luke Rattigan — the inventor of ATMOS who had been betrayed by his Sontaran allies — the Doctor used the Converter to destroy the Sontaran Warship in orbit above the Earth.

TEST YOUR KNOWLEDGE

ANSWERS

The Sontarans
1 (b) 2 (a) 3 (c) 4 (b) 5 (c)

Sontarans and their Allies
1 (c) 2 (a) 3 (b) 4 (a) 5 (b)

The Rutans & Other Sontaran Enemies
1 (b) 2 (c) 3 (a) 4 (c) 5 (a)

Defending the Earth & Attacking the Earth
1 (c) 2 (a) 3 (b) 4 (c) 5 (a)

Weapons and Technology
1 (b) 2 (a) 3 (b) 4 (c) 5 (c)

Sontaran Strategies
1 (b) 2 (c) 3 (a) 4 (c) 5 (b)

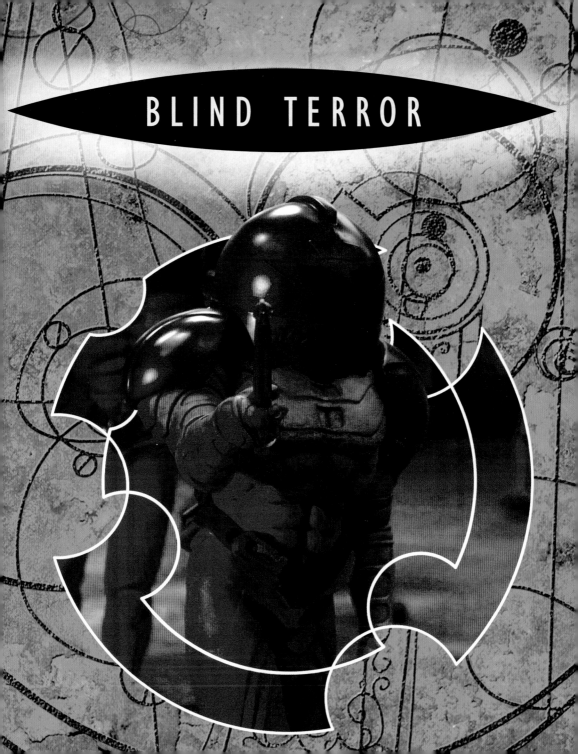

BLIND TERROR

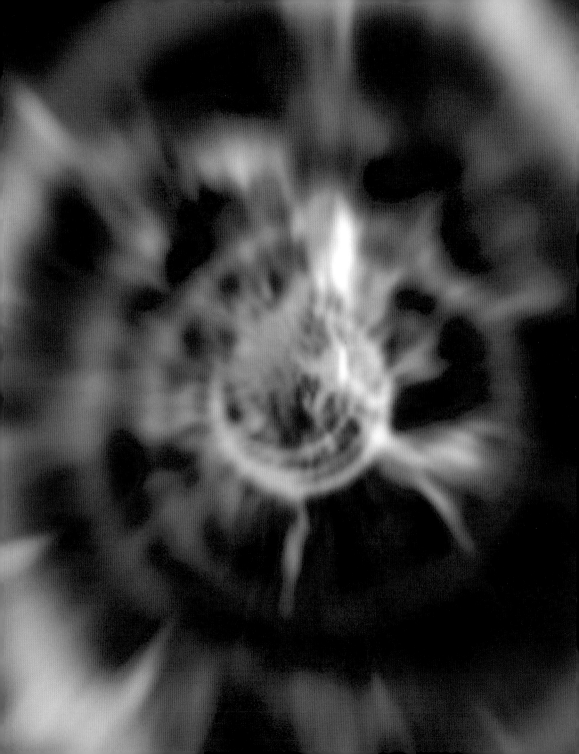

Commander Churl could not resist the hunt. His squadron had ambushed the Rutan convoy in the Sol system while on a routine reconnaissance mission. Churl's ships destroyed three of the four ships in a firestorm of space missiles. The last ship, damaged and trailing smoke and flame, managed to get away.

But Churl had a trace on the damaged engine exhaust. Ordering the rest of his squadron to continue with their mission, he turned to Lieutenant Stavv.

'Follow them down,' he ordered. 'We shall finish this on the planet below.'

Stavv saluted and deftly manoeuvred the small spherical scoutship into orbit over the blue-green planet. 'Picking up a strong heat signature,' he reported. 'The ship must have burned out in the atmosphere and crashed.'

'Then we shall make sure there are no

survivors. And we might obtain useful intelligence from the ship's data systems if they are not too damaged.' He snapped a brisk salute. 'For the greater glory of Sontar!'

'Sontar-ha!' Stavv chanted.

The small scoutship glowed orange and red as it dived through the atmosphere of the small planet called Earth.

The Rutan ship was a burned out shell, buried half in and half out of a primitive stone dwelling. From the surrounding fields, Churl guessed it was a farm.

'The dwelling seems isolated,' Stavv said. 'There should be minimal interference from the native population.'

Churl's grey tongue flicked over his bloodless lips. 'That is good. We shall check the wreckage for survivors.'

There was no sign of life from the farmhouse or the Rutan ship. Stavv waited outside on guard while Churl went into the wrecked command dome of the ship first. The blobby gelatinous green bodies of several dead Rutans were hanging lifeless in their cradles by the burned-out controls.

Churl called Stavv in and together they inspected the computer systems.

'A science ship,' Stavv said as he coaxed one of the screens into life. 'The database contains encrypted reports on Rutan weapons programs and experimental techniques.'

'Break their codes. Access all data and copy it. We shall take it back to Sontar for analysis. This could be a great victory, Lieutenant Stavv.'

'Sir.' Stavv set to work.

Behind him, Churl was walking slowly round the shattered command dome. He paused beside a Rutan cradle. It was hanging loose and empty from its webbed mesh of nutrient pipes. A trail of green liquid splashed across the floor to the door.

'Bring me the data as soon as you have it,' Churl told his Lieutenant. 'And I will hunt down and destroy the Rutan survivor.'

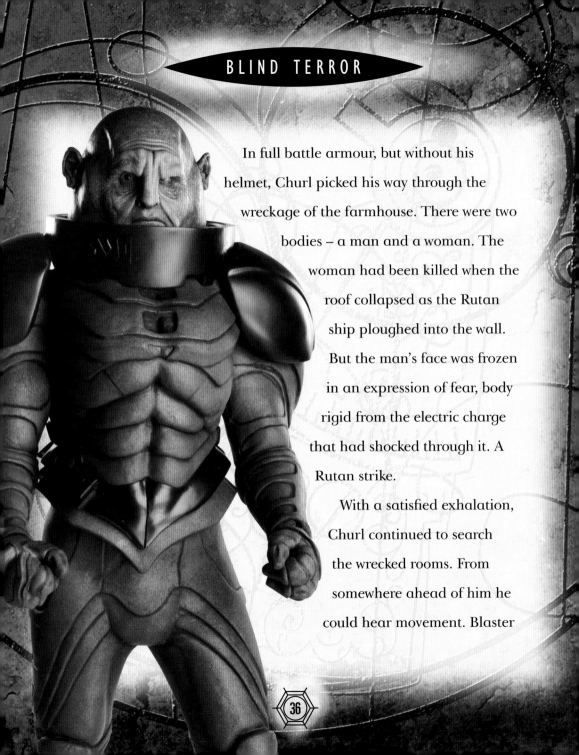

In full battle armour, but without his helmet, Churl picked his way through the wreckage of the farmhouse. There were two bodies – a man and a woman. The woman had been killed when the roof collapsed as the Rutan ship ploughed into the wall. But the man's face was frozen in an expression of fear, body rigid from the electric charge that had shocked through it. A Rutan strike.

With a satisfied exhalation, Churl continued to search the wrecked rooms. From somewhere ahead of him he could hear movement. Blaster

tube poised, Churl made his way silently through to the next room.

A figure was standing there. Churl recognised it at once from his training as a humanoid girl – one of their young. It had long fair hair growing from its head, and was looking round desperately, obviously frightened.

It was a distraction that Churl did not need. He raised the blaster.

Then he hesitated. There was something wrong with the human female. She looked right at him, yet gave no reaction, turning away as if he wasn't there. Churl let out a puzzled breath – and the female turned back towards him.

'Please,' she said. 'I'm just a girl.'

It took Churl's translator unit a moment to analyse the speech and convert it. 'And you are blind,' he replied in her own language.

'I lost my sight years ago,' the girl said quietly, as if ashamed.

'In battle?'

'To illness.'

Churl snarled in contempt. 'Then you have no honour and are of no consequence.' He strode across to her and grabbed her hair. 'And with no eyesight, you cannot tell me where the Rutan coward is hiding.' He pushed her away, and raised his blaster again.

'The animal?'

Churl hesitated. 'Animal? Explain.'

'After the fire, the noise and the heat. There was an animal. I heard it.' The girl broke off and wiped her sightless eyes. 'It killed father, I think. He was crying for mother, and the animal…' She shook her head. 'I hid. I ran and hid. I couldn't see, I couldn't save them. You were right. I have no honour.'

In three swift strides, Churl was beside the girl again. He grabbed her arm roughly. 'The Rutan – this animal – where is it now?'

She was shaking with fear, her voice trembling. 'I heard it leave. A strange noise, as if it was dragging rather than walking.'

'Where is it?!'

'It went to the barn.'

Churl pushed the girl away from him, towards the hole ripped through the wall of the building. 'Show me. Then perhaps I shall let you live.'

The barn was a separate small outbuilding. It was undamaged. The heavy wooden doors stood slightly open. Inside, all was dark. A perfect place for the cowardly Rutan to hide, Churl thought.

'It went in there?'

'I heard the door. The hinges creak when it opens. I know all the sounds of the farm.'

Churl pushed the girl aside. He raised his blaster and warily approached the barn. The Rutan might be an inferior coward, but its electric charge could still be fatal, even through full battle armour. Without his helmet, Churl felt vulnerable. But he also felt elated. He would meet his enemy face to face and he would defeat it.

The doors opened outwards, and Churl flung one aside. He threw a tiny pellet into the barn – a flare. The light was sudden and brilliant, but Churl shielded his eyes until it died down. Then he leaped through the doorway, swinging his blaster to cover every corner.

There was still enough light from the flare for him to see the whole building clearly. It was little more than a shed – square and open, with nowhere to hide. And it was empty.

With a snarl of rage and frustration, Churl turned back to the girl.

But she had gone.

Like the barn, the Rutan ship was empty. Churl stood in the doorway and called for Lieutenant Stavv. There was no answer.

The only sign of life was the green glow of the computer terminal that Stavv had been using. Churl scrolled through the data that Stavv had left displayed. It was a report on a new Rutan development. The ability for a Rutan to disguise itself as another creature.

Churl spun round, checking again he was alone, then he read through the report again. The Metamorphosis Technique, as it was called, was new and still experimental. It was far from perfect. The Rutan needed a genetic sample of the body it would copy – a small portion of blood or tissue would suffice.

But even then it seemed there were still problems. The Rutan could not maintain the new body shape for very long, and needed to revert to its true form to kill with its electric 'sting'. More importantly, the shape it assumed was never perfect. In all the experiments so far, there was always a defect – a physical difference. Something not quite correct, where the copying process had not worked.

Churl walked slowly out of the wrecked Rutan ship and headed back towards the farmhouse. He wanted to know what had happened to Lieutenant Stavv, and he wanted to find the human girl whose eyes did not work…

He found Stavv first. The Sontaran lieutenant was staggering from the ruins of the farmhouse. He was trailing his left leg, limping badly. He almost collapsed when he saw Churl waiting outside the Rutan ship.

'Sir!' Stavv gasped. 'The Rutan. I came to find you, to warn you. The Rutan was waiting for me in the building. It got my leg.' He stopped a short way in front of Churl and saluted. 'You read the report on the screen.'

Churl nodded. 'Have you seen the human girl?'

'She got close to me. Too close before I realised what she was. I should have realised sooner.' He lowered his eyes. 'I have failed, sir.'

'Her eyesight. A physical imperfection,' Churl said slowly. 'The Rutan maintains its disguise so it can get close and attack. The strategy of a coward.'

'The Rutans have no honour,' Stavv agreed. 'No stomach for close combat.'

'It thinks it can fool us,' Churl said. He drew a stubby tubular device from his belt. 'But to defeat it, we had best be on our guard.' He aimed the device at Stavv's leg. 'The tissue rectifier will heal your wound.

Then together we shall hunt down this craven creature.'

Stavv took a limping step backwards. 'No, sir. I would rather bear my wounds with pride. I allowed the Rutan to get close enough to attack. Let me now destroy it as it left me. I wear my wounds as a symbol of honour and bravery.'

Churl hesitated for a moment. Then he lowered the tissue rectifier. 'Very well.' He was looking past Stavv, towards the barn where he had last seen the human girl. 'You will not have long to wait until combat is joined.'

Stavv turned to watch as Churl strode past him … towards the fair-haired girl standing in front of the barn. She was holding a primitive percussion weapon. As Churl approached she struggled to keep the heavy gun aimed at him.

'I can hear you, whatever you are,' she said, her voice full of fear. The gun was wavering as she guessed where Churl was standing. Behind him, Churl could hear Stavv dragging his wounded leg as he approached.

'You think you can defeat a Sontaran warrior with your primitive weapon?' Churl demanded. 'When you cannot even see your enemy?' He took a step closer to her. 'Your quarrel is surely with the creature that killed your parent humans. Not with me or my lieutenant. Revenge – isn't that what you want?'

The gun was juddering in the girl's hands as she struggled to hold it still and point it in the direction of Churl's voice.

Slowly Churl raised his own hand. He took aim at the girl's head. And fired.

But it wasn't a blaster he was holding. It was the tissue rectifier.

'You wish to take revenge on the creature that killed your family?' Churl said, his voice quieter and gentler now as the girl blinked in the sudden sunlight. 'Then do so. Kill it now!'

Churl stepped aside as the girl stared back at him, horrified. Her pupils dilated

and focused as her eyesight returned, her retinas rebuilt by the tissue rectifier. Churl could only imagine what she must be thinking as she watched Stavv's brutal, powerful shape melt and dissolve into the gelatinous green blob of a Rutan. Its deadly tentacles were already reaching for Churl. He knew he could not draw his blaster, turn, aim and fire quickly enough to stop the Rutan killing him.

But the girl could. Already facing the Rutan, she brought the gun up and pulled the trigger.

Tiny pieces of lead shot from the flintlock weapon and sprayed across the Rutan, tearing into its fragile flesh.

Brushing stray lead shot from his arm, Churl turned to face his enemy. 'Stavv would never have been bested by a blind human girl,' he sneered. 'You hid in the shadows outside the ship and attacked him from behind, then dragged his corpse away to take its form.'

'We die with the honour of our race,' the Rutan gasped as its body disintegrated.

'Honour?' Churl laughed. 'You have no concept of honour. You thought Stavv would bear the scars of defeat? No – wounds should be a badge of victory, or they should be healed ready for the next battle.' He kicked at the dead green mess now lying at his feet. 'There is honour and glory here today, but you have neither.'

There was a metallic click from behind him, and Churl swung round. The girl was pointing the gun at him now.

Churl walked calmly towards her. 'Such a weapon affords only one shot without complicated reloading. But you used it well. I thank you, and I ask a favour.'

'What are you?' the girl stammered.

'If you find the body of my lieutenant, bury it with due ceremony. He deserves no less.' Churl turned to go. But then he hesitated and turned back. He thumped his clenched right fist into his left shoulder. 'I salute you. You have avenged your parents and done so with honour.

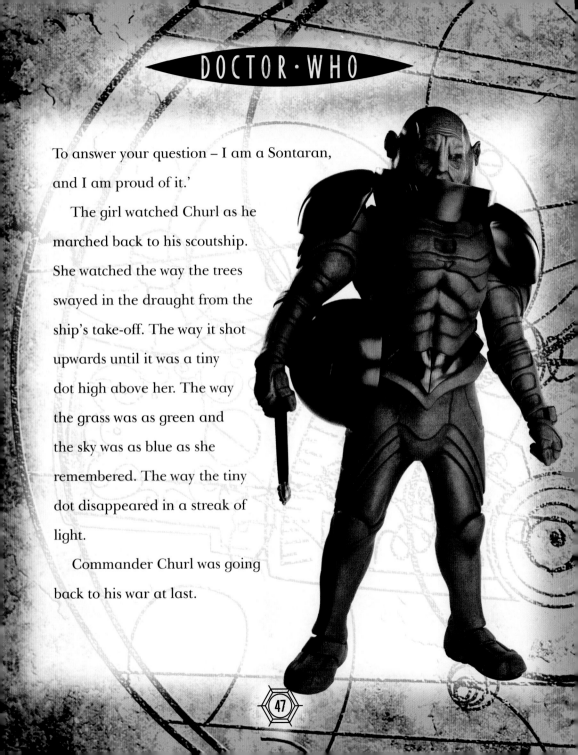

To answer your question – I am a Sontaran, and I am proud of it.'

The girl watched Churl as he marched back to his scoutship. She watched the way the trees swayed in the draught from the ship's take-off. The way it shot upwards until it was a tiny dot high above her. The way the grass was as green and the sky was as blue as she remembered. The way the tiny dot disappeared in a streak of light.

Commander Churl was going back to his war at last.